WHAT ON EARTH?

Water

BART AND LYNN KING

High Noon Books
Novato, California

Editor: Deb Akers
Interior Illustrations: Cynthia Coverston
Cover Design: Bonni Gatter

International Standard Book Number: 978-1-57128-434-1

16 15 14 13 12 11 10 09 08 07
10 09 08 07 06 05 04 03 02 01

Contents

CHAPTER 1

Water Break!

Beep! Beep! Beep!

Val rolled over and tapped the clock by her bed. It said 6:45.

Time to get up, Val said to herself. She had been having a good dream, too. She wanted to sleep more, but she knew she had to get up. There were some clothes she had to wash before school started.

First, Val went into the bathroom. She turned on the water to wash her face. But no water came out.

"That is odd," she said with a shrug. Still, there was time for a quick bath. Val turned on the water for the tub.

No water poured into the tub!

Val was still sleepy. Was this just a bad dream? Just then, a cry came from downstairs. It was Max. He was always the first one up. "I can't boil eggs," Max yelled. "What is up with our water?"

Now Val heard sounds from her mom and dad's room. Her dad's low voice came from the room.

"What is going on here?" he asked.

This is a bad way to start the week, Val

thought. She went downstairs. Max was holding a cooking pot. He looked upset.

Mr. and Mrs. Chase joined Max and Val by the sink.

"Kids, we have bad news," their mom said. "There is NO water."

"Uh-oh," Val said. "My P.E. clothes are all dirty. I have to wash them before I go to my class!"

"And what about my eggs!" cried Max.

"And I can't brush my teeth," said Dad. "It looks like we will all have to wait."

Mom made a face. "This is like a bad dream," she said.

Val got ready for school. It did not feel

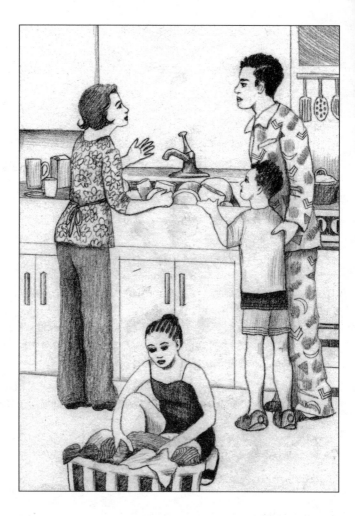

"There is NO water."

right to start her day without water. She thought, "I'll just have to wait, like Dad said."

At school, Val told Tess about the water. "It is like when the lights go out. Only this is worse!" Val moaned.

Tess was shocked. "So where did your water go?" she asked.

Mr. Chase had made a call. The water pipe going into Val's house had broken. It would be fixed that day.

"With no water, our whole house stopped working," Val said. "I did not think about how much we need water."

Tess spoke up. "Do you think we should do our next film on water?"

They were part of a film team with Sam and Nate. The four took a film class taught by Ms. Reese.

Sam and Nate were walking near the two girls. They heard the last bit of what Tess was saying.

"Water?" Sam said. "Could there be anything more dull?"

Nate shook his head. "You are saying that just because you only drink pop," he said. "Good, pure water is the best!"

"Water has no taste or smell!" Sam said. "And it is clear, like glass. How boring is that?"

Val smiled. Her teacher Mr. Kim had taught her a lot about water. "Sam," she said, "you cannot feel that way about water."

"Why not?" Sam asked.

"Because water is a big part of you. The water leaves when you sweat or breathe. Think about when you breathe on glass. Your breath leaves a fog on the glass. That is water!"

Nate nodded. He had been in Mr. Kim's class, too. "That is right. Your arms and legs and head—all of you—is mostly water. So if you do not like water, you do not like yourself!"

"And we all know that is not true," teased Tess.

Sam laughed. He knew when he was beaten. "OK, we can do the film on water," he said. He looked down and walked away.

Nate, Val, and Tess traded looks. "Where are you going?" Val asked.

Sam acted like he was mad. But like always, he was joking. "If you must know, I have to get a drink of water."

CHAPTER 2

Water Way

That day in film class, the team worked on a plan. What should their film on water show? What did folks need to see and learn about?

"Well, we have to show water," Nate said.

"But there is more than one kind of water," Val said. "Clouds in the sky are made of water. And ice is water, too."

"Yeah, and water is water," said Sam with a smirk. "But you have no water at home. How do you know so much about it?"

Nate and Val both said, "Mr. Kim!" They laughed. "Great brains think the same," said Nate.

Tess kept the team on the job. "The water in the clouds gets back to the earth sooner or later. It can come as rain, snow, hail, fog, or dew."

Nate nodded. "The news said it would rain today. We can film that. If we are lucky, we might get a rainbow!"

The team had its plan. Even Sam seemed to like the topic. "I still would rather drink pop than water," he said.

Val rode her skateboard home from school. There was a big truck parked out front. A deep trench went from the street up to her house. Workers were putting a new pipe down in the hole.

A worker warned Val. "Don't get too close to the trench," he said.

Val stepped back. "All we needed was a new pipe?" she asked.

The worker nodded. "Yes, the other one was shot. It was about 80 years old. It was time for a new one."

"I know water comes to our house in this pipe," Val said. "But where does the water come from?"

The man pointed out to the street. "There is a bigger pipe under the road. Your water comes

*A worker warned Val. "Don't get too close
to the trench," he said.*

from there."

Val frowned. "Yes, but where does that pipe get its water?" The man scratched his head. "Oh, I see. You mean where does the water come from in the first place!" He told Val that water could come from one of many places. Not all towns got their water the same way. Some used water from springs deep under the ground. That water had to be pumped out.

But Val's water came from a place called Lone Crow Lake. It was about 30 miles away. Lone Crow had a dam at one end. This dam moved the lake water into a big holding tank. From there, a large pipe sent the water into town.

What the man said was a big help. Val told him about the film she and her friends were making. The worker gave Val a card. "Beth Wells is in charge of things at Lone Crow," he said. "You should talk to her. She can tell you what you need to know. Good luck on your film project," said the worker.

"Thanks," Val said. "Losing our pipe was a good thing. It showed how much we need water."

After that, Val went inside. She looked at the card and grabbed her phone. Beth Wells picked up after one ring. She said she was glad to tell Val about Lone Crow. She could only talk for a few minutes. Then she would have to go to a meeting.

Beth had a big job. She had to make sure the water was pure and safe. The water came from a lake. It had to be cleaned and made more pure. Then it had to be tested. After that, it flowed to town by a large pipe.

Once it got there, the water went into smaller and smaller pipes. There were over 1,000 miles of water pipes running under the town. All of them got their water from Lone Crow Lake.

"One more thing," said Val. "Where does the water in the lake come from?"

"It gets most of its water from rain," Beth said. "Creeks and streams feed water into the lake, too."

"But what if we don't get much rain?" Val asked.

"In the hot months, more water gets used," Beth said. "Folks drink more. And they water their plants a lot. But you are right. That is when we have little rain. So we try to save water in the rainy times. That way, we have some left for the dry times."

"Can my team film the Lone Crow holding tank?" Val asked.

"I'm very sad to say no," Beth said. "We do not let anyone in to see the tank. It is one way of keeping the water pure and safe."

Val thanked Beth and hung up the phone.

Just then there was a knock on the door. It was the worker she had talked to before. He said that the new water pipe was done. Val could turn on the water again.

Yes! thought Val. *At last!* Val thanked the worker and closed the door. She had a lot to do.

She put her dirty PE clothes in the wash. And once the wash was done, she took a long, hot bath.

CHAPTER 3

Water Saver

Sam looked down at his clipboard.

"Turn right here," he said. "Thanks for driving us today, Mr. Sharp."

Mr. Sharp glanced over from the steering wheel. "I am glad to help. But where are we going?"

Tess said, "A few places, Dad. I did a Web search. I learned about places that use a lot of water. Sam and I want to film these spots."

"But we are now outside town," said Mr.

Sharp. The car was on a dirt road. There were farms on each side. Green plants grew neatly in rows.

"I know," said Tess. "This is our first stop." She and Sam got out of the car. They got set to film. At first, Mr. Sharp just stood there. He did not see why they were there. But then he spotted something. Hoses were shooting water over the fields.

"Farms use 80 percent of all our water. They need it to grow plants," Tess said. "So this seemed like a good place to start." She and Sam filmed some good shots. Then they packed up and headed back to town.

"Here is something you may not know,"

said Mr. Sharp. "There is water in this car."

Sam laughed. "Nice try, Mr. Sharp. Cars run on gas."

Mr. Sharp smiled. "Cars do run on gas," he said. "A car burns the gas to go. This makes the car hot under the hood. And so we put water in the car, too. The water helps keep the car cool."

"Oh," said Sam. "Now I get it."

Tess looked at their clipboard. "Speaking of cooling off, we are close to our next stop."

The car was nearing a park. There were jets of water spraying out of the ground. Little kids were running back and forth. They were laughing and getting wet. Older folks were there, too. They were watching and smiling.

Mr. Sharp stopped the car. Tess got out and opened the trunk.

"Look at all that water!" Sam said. "It looks like a lot of fun."

"It looks like a lot of water waste, too," said Mr. Sharp.

Tess shot some film of the scene. She said, "It's not wasted. The water goes down a drain after it sprays. These jets re-use all of the water."

"Oops," said Mr. Sharp.

Tess and Sam and Mr. Sharp had fun that day. They drove around and found water being used in many places. They filmed at the ice skating rink. Sam stepped out on the ice and slipped. Tess made sure to get this on film. As they headed home, Mr. Sharp pulled the car to the curb.

"Check out that yard," Mr. Sharp said.

Sam and Tess looked. "What should we see?" Sam asked.

Mr. Sharp got out of the car. Tess gave Sam a look and a shrug. "Let's go," she said. The three of them walked up to the gate. They looked in and saw an older man holding a bucket.

"Hello," said Mr. Sharp. "We saw your garden from the car. We would like to ask you how you keep everything so green and lush."

The man invited them in. He was standing next to a bathtub in his garden. It was full of water.

He was standing next to a bathtub in his garden.
It was full of water.

"You must have seen our tubs," the man said. "We try to save as much water as we can." He walked out front with them. He pointed to a drain pipe. The pipe came down from the roof. Then it went into a big tub. "When it rains, the water goes in here," said the man. "We save it for later."

"Is it clean?" asked Sam. "Do you drink it?"

The man shook his head. "Oh, no. It's not for drinking," he said. "It's for watering our plants. We use a bucket to take the water to the plants. Carrying the water helps the plants, and me, too."

Sam made a face.

The man looked at Sam. He said, "The plants stay green and I stay fit!" He lifted the bucket full of water, and smiled.

Tess and Sam laughed.

CHAPTER 4

Water Works

In class, Tess and Sam showed their film to Nate and Val.

"I like the man who saves rain water," said Nate.

Sam rolled his eyes. "Why save rain water? He could get as much from the tap," he said.

Tess spoke up. "For one thing, it keeps his water bill low."

Val thought back to her talk with Beth Wells. "Plus, it saves water for the town. That is a good thing in the hot months," she said.

The film they had shot made Nate think. He now knew where water came from. But where did it go when it was used? Where did it go after it went down the drain?

The rest of the group put their work away. They were talking about this year's Spring Fling. This was put on by teachers, moms, and dads. It took place right before spring break. Folks had been talking about the Spring Fling a lot. It would be at the Water Park this year. This was a place with many water slides and swimming pools.

"We could do two things at once!" said Val. "We could swim and work on our film!"

"Wow," said Sam. "Doing homework in our swimsuits is some plan!"

Nate's mind was somewhere else. He was still thinking about waste water and where it went. He sat while his pals talked. He used the team laptop. On the Web, he did a search. He found that there was a waste water plant in town. Nate sent the plant an e-mail. In it, he said who he was. He told about the film his team was working on, too.

This note came back quickly.

From: Waste Water Plant

To: Nate Parks

Subject: Your film

Thank you for writing to us. We are in

charge of all waste water in town. It is a very big job.

Any water that goes down a drain or pipe and leaves a house comes to us. We take the water and make it pure again. Then we can put the water back into use.

We would love to have you come. And, yes, you may bring a pal. I will show you the plant. You can film as much as you like. How does March 21 at 10:45 sound?

Mr. Will Poole

The e-mail made Nate smile. He looked up at his three pals. "Who wants to go with me to the waste water plant?" he asked.

Val and Tess traded looks. They shook their

29

heads. That left Sam. Sam gave a nod. "That sounds good," he said. Sam was always game to go somewhere.

"All right, then. It looks like it's Sam and me," Nate said. "And Sam?"

"Huh?" Sam asked. He was thinking about the Spring Fling again.

Nate smiled. "You won't need your swimsuit."

CHAPTER 5

Waste Water

The bus came to a stop. Nate and Sam grabbed their stuff and got off. This was the place. The sign out front said Waste Water Plant. Sam and Nate went inside. A neatly dressed man met them.

"Hi, I'm Mr. Poole," he said. "You must be Nate and Sam! Come on. I will show you the plant. And please ask me anything you want." Mr. Poole was not wasting time. He led the two boys down a hallway.

Mr. Poole took Nate and Sam into an odd space. It was a big room. The room was like a film set. It had a small house in it. There was a living room and a bathroom. There was a place to cook. And there was a fake yard with a hose. The house walls were cut out in spots. This meant you could see right into the house.

"We built this set as a teaching tool," said Mr. Poole. "This is a Waste Water Plant. But we hate to see water wasted!"

Sam wanted to get this on film. "Could you say that one more time, Mr. Poole?" he asked. "We would like to put you in our film."

"Good call," said Nate. He gave Sam a nod.

Mr. Poole pointed to the bathroom sink.

"We all know how big a jug of milk is. But get this. Say you are brushing your teeth. You let the water run while you do it. You will use up to two jugs of water by doing that! Plus, your sink might have a drip. That can waste eight jugs of water in one day."

Next, Mr. Poole took a seat by the sink. "Flushing uses a lot of water, too. For most homes, it uses over 20 jugs a day."

Nate put his hand up. "What uses the next most water?"

"Inside the house, it is the washer," said Mr. Poole. "But there is something outside we should look at. It uses more water than all the things indoors." Mr. Poole led them through a cut-out wall. He now stood in the fake yard. He pointed to a hose. It was curled up like a green snake.

"Many houses have lawns. And most of a house's water goes to the lawn," Mr. Poole said.

"Wow," said Sam, still filming. "Grass must be really thirsty."

"Is there a way to get that water use down?" asked Nate.

Mr. Poole gave a nod. He said one way was not to water lawns in the daytime. Then the water would not dry up in the sun. "But the best way is to not have a lawn," he said. "Many plants do not need as much water as grass, but still look nice."

"Cut!" said Sam, taking a break. "Mr. Poole, you are a real pro."

Mr. Poole smiled and bowed. "Thank you, Sam! Now we will look at more parts of this plant." He led the boys outside. In back of the plant were large pools of water. Nate and Sam stood and looked into a pool. They held onto a rail.

"The water that gets flushed or poured down the drain comes here," said Mr. Poole. He said there were pipes under all the houses in town. Some pipes brought water into the house. More pipes took waste water from the house. Those pipes led here, to this plant. That way,

Nate and Sam stood and looked into a pool.
They held onto a rail.

the plant could make the water pure again.

Some waste water needed a little help to be pure. It could be strained through a screen and cleaned. But some waste water had a lot of stuff in it. That was why they had these pools.

Mr. Poole said that waste water was pumped into a pool. Then the waste water sat there for a while. Any sludge in the water would sink or float to the top. The waste on top was skimmed off. Then all the water was pumped to a clean new pool.

Mr. Poole showed them a pond that was being filled. "We let the water sit some more. And we clean it again. Each time we do this, the water gets more pure," he said.

"So that is why you have so many ponds," said Nate.

Sam and Nate learned more. Some water was treated for just a short while. That water was sent to farms. There it was used to water plants. But some of the water would go into a stream. This water had to be much cleaner. There were many cleaning steps for making this water pure.

Nate and Sam had learned a lot. "Thank you for the tour," Nate said to Mr. Poole. "We got some great film. Anyone who watches it will find out something new."

"It's true," said Sam. "Most folks do not know any of this." Then he leaned close to one of the pools. He sniffed the air. "Dude!" he said to Nate. "Now I know why you told me not to bring my swimsuit."

CHAPTER 6

Spring Fling

The day of the Spring Fling was here. Everyone climbed on buses. Then they drove to the Water Park. There were water rides, pools, flumes, chutes, and games. Nate, Sam, Tess, and Val were climbing a long set of stairs. These led to the top of the huge water slide. It was called The Plunge.

It was sunny, but Nate looked pale. "Are you okay?" Tess asked.

"I don't like high places," he said. "This is

safe, right?"

"There are lifeguards all over the place," Sam said. "But you might get sucked down a whirlpool."

The four of them made it to the top. Nate wanted to go first. That way he could get The Plunge over with.

"Are you all set?" Val asked. Nate was in front of her.

"No, not yet!" Nate said. He was trying to get seated on a foam pad.

"I can't hear you!" Val yelled. She winked at Tess and Sam. Then she gave Nate a little push. They all watched. Nate went down the long, winding slide. His yell got fainter and fainter. He was moving fast.

"They say you go 40 miles an hour down that slide," said Val.

"Now Nate can ask a lifeguard where the water goes," said Sam.

One by one, Val, Sam and Tess followed Nate down The Plunge.

There was only a bit of work left to do. Soon, the team finished the film. They put the new film on a disc. Then they gave it to Ms. Reese. She liked to see the films before the class did.

The next day, it was time to show the film to the whole class. The team sat in the front. Ms. Reese stood up.

"I watched this film with a teacher," she said. "He wants to speak to the team that made it."

"Uh-oh," said Sam.

Ms. Reese smiled. "The teacher was Mr. Kim. He liked the film very much. He wants to know if he can show it to his class. It will be a big help when they learn about water."

Tess and Sam gave each other high fives. Nate and Val were proud, too. Good old Mr. Kim!